This book belongs to:

_____

_____

Phone:

_____

Email:

_____

Christian
Reading
Journal

Created by

Cathryn Brown

Sienna Bay Press

Sienna Bay Press
PO Box 158582
Nashville, TN 37215

www.cathrynbrown.com

Copyright © 2016 Shannon L. Brown

ISBN: 978-1-945527-28-9

Unless otherwise noted, all scripture quotations are taken from the New American Standard Bible.

Scripture quotations taken from the New American Standard Bible® (NASB), Copyright © 1960, 1962, 1963, 1968, 1971, 1972, 1973, 1975, 1977, 1995 by The Lockman Foundation
Used by permission. www.Lockman.org

Scripture quotations marked (NIV) are taken from the Holy Bible, New International Version®, NIV®. Copyright © 1973, 1978, 1984, 2011 by Biblica, Inc.™ Used by permission of Zondervan. All rights reserved worldwide. www.zondervan.com The "NIV" and "New International Version" are trademarks registered in the United States Patent and Trademark Office by Biblica, Inc.™

Table of Contents

Dear Readers,

If you're like me, you've read a book and later not remembered the name of either it or the author. I've created this journal as a fun, easy method for keeping track of the books you read and want to read.

I've also included some fun ways to make notes about the books. The type is large enough to be easily readable after long stretches of reading. (You do that, don't you? I want to read one more page, but it turns into quite a few pages more.)

When you loan or borrow a book, note it on the pages provided so you don't forget. A bookplate is included in the front so your journal can easily be returned if misplaced. The year or date range of this journal can be noted on the blank at the bottom of that page.

Books are a great joy and, I believe, a blessing from God. You'll find Bible verses about joy and blessings throughout this journal. (I felt awesome joy as I gathered the verses!)

I hope the next book you read blesses you.

Cathryn Brown
Neh 8:10

Then the LORD answered me and said, "Record the vision And inscribe it on tablets, That the one who reads it may run.

Habakkuk 2:2

My Favorite Authors

When you discover a writer you love,
write his or her name here!

_____

_____

_____

_____

_____

_____

_____

_____

_____

_____

_____

_____

_____

_____

_____

_____

_____

_____

_____

_____

_____

I read . . .

Title: _____

Author: _____

Sub-genre: _____

Date Published: _____

Date Finished: _____

Rating ○○○○○○○○○○
1   10

Where I read this book:

_____

_____

_____

How I discovered or received this book:

_____

_____

My favorite spiritual moment in the book:

_____

_____

_____

_____

"For I know the plans I have for you," declares the Lord,
*"plans to prosper you and not to harm you,
plans to give you hope and a future."* (NIV)
Jeremiah 29:11

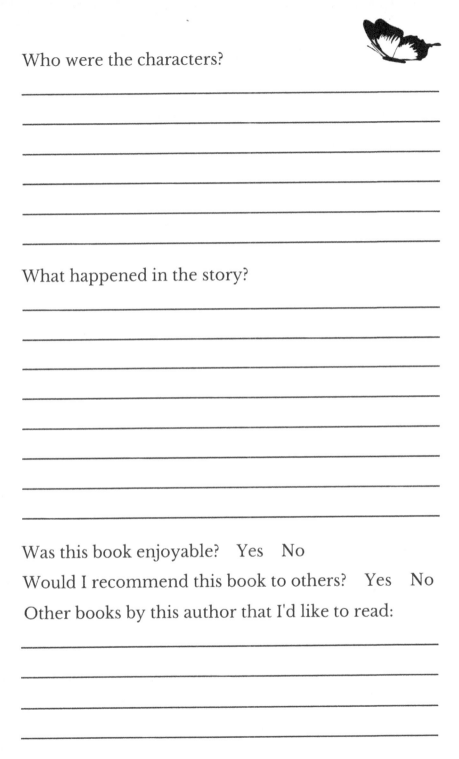

Who were the characters?

_____

_____

_____

_____

_____

_____

What happened in the story?

_____

_____

_____

_____

_____

_____

_____

Was this book enjoyable?   Yes   No

Would I recommend this book to others?   Yes   No

Other books by this author that I'd like to read:

_____

_____

_____

_____

I read . . .

Title: _____

Author: _____

Sub-genre: _____

Date Published: _____

Date Finished: _____

Rating ○○○○○○○○○○
          1   10

Where I read this book:

_____

_____

_____

How I discovered or received this book:

_____

_____

My favorite spiritual moment in the book:

_____

_____

_____

_____

Praise the LORD.How good it is to sing praises to our God,
how pleasant and fitting to praise him!
Psalm 147:1

Who were the characters?

_____

_____

_____

_____

_____

_____

What happened in the story?

_____

_____

_____

_____

_____

_____

_____

Was this book enjoyable?   Yes   No

Would I recommend this book to others?   Yes   No

Other books by this author that I'd like to read:

_____

_____

_____

_____

I read . . .

Title:_____

Author: _____

Sub-genre:_____

Date Published: _____

Date Finished:_____

Rating ○○○○○○○○○○
      1   10

Where I read this book:

_____

_____

_____

How I discovered or received this book:

_____

_____

My favorite spiritual moment in the book:

_____

_____

_____

This is the day which the LORD has made;
Let us rejoice and be glad in it.
Psalm 118:24

Who were the characters?

_____

_____

_____

_____

_____

What happened in the story?

_____

_____

_____

_____

_____

_____

Was this book enjoyable?   Yes   No

Would I recommend this book to others?   Yes   No

Other books by this author that I'd like to read:

_____

_____

_____

_____

I read . . .

Title:_____

Author: _____

Sub-genre:_____

Date Published:_____

Date Finished:_____

Rating ○○○○○○○○○○
          1   10

Where I read this book:

_____

_____

_____

How I discovered or received this book:

_____

_____

My favorite spiritual moment in the book:

_____

_____

_____

_____

The LORD has done great things for us,
and we are filled with joy. (NIV)
Psalm 126:3

Who were the characters?

_____

_____

_____

_____

_____

_____

What happened in the story?

_____

_____

_____

_____

_____

_____

Was this book enjoyable?   Yes   No

Would I recommend this book to others?   Yes   No

Other books by this author that I'd like to read:

_____

_____

_____

_____

I read . . .

Title: _____

Author: _____

Sub-genre: _____

Date Published: _____

Date Finished: _____

Rating ◯◯◯◯◯◯◯◯◯◯
       1   10

Where I read this book:

_____

_____

_____

How I discovered or received this book:

_____

_____

My favorite spiritual moment in the book:

_____

_____

_____

_____

Rejoice in the Lord always; again I will say, rejoice!
Philippians 4:4

Who were the characters?

_____

_____

_____

_____

_____

_____

What happened in the story?

_____

_____

_____

_____

_____

_____

_____

Was this book enjoyable?   Yes   No

Would I recommend this book to others?   Yes   No

Other books by this author that I'd like to read:

_____

_____

_____

_____

I read . . .

Title: _____

Author: _____

Sub-genre: _____

Date Published: _____

Date Finished: _____

Rating ○○○○○○○○○○
       1   10

Where I read this book:

_____

_____

_____

How I discovered or received this book:

_____

_____

My favorite spiritual moment in the book:

_____

_____

_____

I was glad when they said to me,
"Let us go to the house of the LORD."
Psalm 122:1

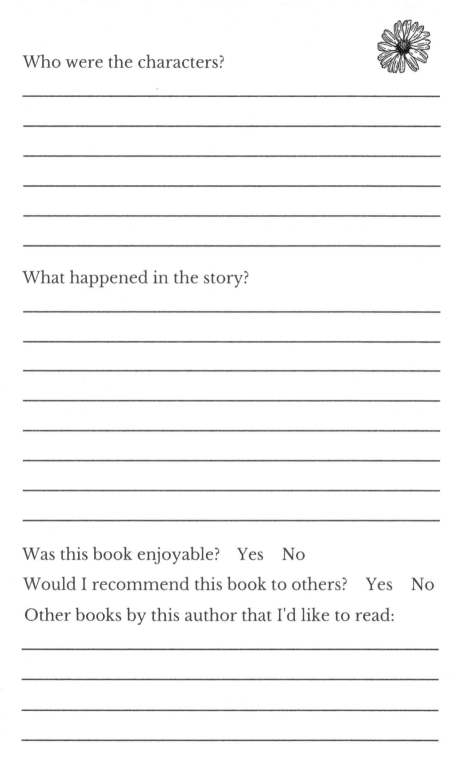

Who were the characters?

_____

_____

_____

_____

_____

_____

What happened in the story?

_____

_____

_____

_____

_____

_____

_____

Was this book enjoyable?   Yes   No

Would I recommend this book to others?   Yes   No

Other books by this author that I'd like to read:

_____

_____

_____

_____

I read . . .

Title: _____

Author: _____

Sub-genre: _____

Date Published: _____

Date Finished: _____

Rating ○○○○○○○○○○
1   10

Where I read this book:

_____

_____

_____

How I discovered or received this book:

_____

_____

My favorite spiritual moment in the book:

_____

_____

_____

_____

Therefore my heart is glad and my glory rejoices . . .
Psalm 16:9

Who were the characters?

_____

_____

_____

_____

_____

_____

What happened in the story?

_____

_____

_____

_____

_____

_____

_____

Was this book enjoyable?   Yes   No

Would I recommend this book to others?   Yes   No

Other books by this author that I'd like to read:

_____

_____

_____

_____

I read . . .

Title: _____

Author: _____

Sub-genre: _____

Date Published: _____

Date Finished: _____

Rating ⭕⭕⭕⭕⭕⭕⭕⭕⭕
        1   10

Where I read this book:

_____

_____

_____

How I discovered or received this book:

_____

_____

My favorite spiritual moment in the book:

_____

_____

_____

Behold, I am with you and will keep you wherever you go,
and will bring you back to this land; for I will not leave you
until I have done what I have promised you."
Genesis 28:15

Who were the characters?

_____

_____

_____

_____

_____

_____

What happened in the story?

_____

_____

_____

_____

_____

_____

Was this book enjoyable?   Yes   No

Would I recommend this book to others?   Yes   No

Other books by this author that I'd like to read:

_____

_____

_____

_____

I read . . .

Title:_____

Author: _____

Sub-genre:_____

Date Published: _____

Date Finished:_____

Rating $\bigcirc\bigcirc\bigcirc\bigcirc\bigcirc\bigcirc\bigcirc\bigcirc\bigcirc\bigcirc$
      1   10

Where I read this book:

_____

_____

_____

How I discovered or received this book:

_____

_____

My favorite spiritual moment in the book:

_____

_____

_____

You will make known to me the path of life;
In Your presence is fullness of joy;
In Your right hand there are pleasures forever.
Psalm 16:11

Who were the characters?

_____

_____

_____

_____

_____

_____

What happened in the story?

_____

_____

_____

_____

_____

_____

_____

Was this book enjoyable?   Yes   No

Would I recommend this book to others?   Yes   No

Other books by this author that I'd like to read:

_____

_____

_____

_____

I read . . .

Title: _____

Author: _____

Sub-genre: _____

Date Published: _____

Date Finished: _____

Rating ○○○○○○○○○○
          1   10

Where I read this book:

_____

_____

_____

How I discovered or received this book:

_____

_____

My favorite spiritual moment in the book:

_____

_____

_____

_____

Sing joyfully to the LORD, you righteous;
it is fitting for the upright to praise him. (NIV)
Psalm 33:1

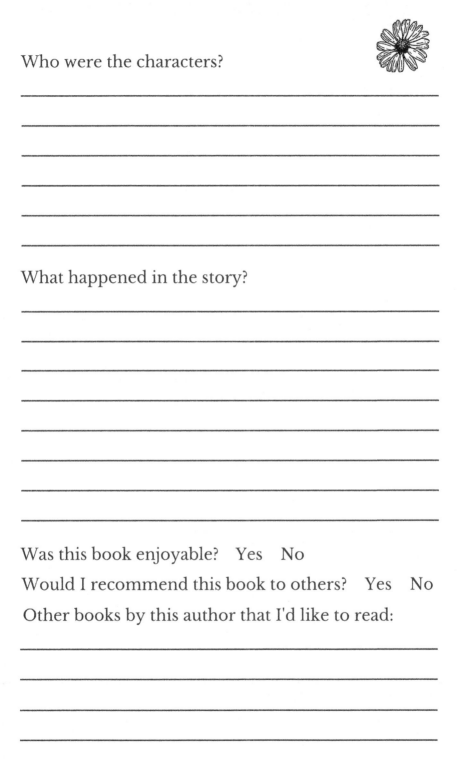

Who were the characters?

_____

_____

_____

_____

_____

_____

What happened in the story?

_____

_____

_____

_____

_____

_____

Was this book enjoyable?   Yes   No

Would I recommend this book to others?   Yes   No

Other books by this author that I'd like to read:

_____

_____

_____

_____

I read . . .

Title: _____

Author: _____

Sub-genre: _____

Date Published: _____

Date Finished: _____

Rating ○○○○○○○○○
      1   10

Where I read this book:

_____

_____

_____

How I discovered or received this book:

_____

_____

My favorite spiritual moment in the book:

_____

_____

_____

_____

And they, after worshiping Him,
returned to Jerusalem with great joy . . .
Luke 24:52

Who were the characters?

_____

_____

_____

_____

_____

_____

What happened in the story?

_____

_____

_____

_____

_____

_____

Was this book enjoyable?   Yes   No

Would I recommend this book to others?   Yes   No

Other books by this author that I'd like to read:

_____

_____

_____

_____

I read . . .

Title: _____

Author: _____

Sub-genre: _____

Date Published: _____

Date Finished: _____

Rating ◯◯◯◯◯◯◯◯◯◯
         1   10

Where I read this book:

_____

_____

_____

How I discovered or received this book:

_____

_____

My favorite spiritual moment in the book:

_____

_____

_____

_____

Therefore you will joyously draw water
From the springs of salvation.
Isaiah 12:3

24

Who were the characters?

_____

_____

_____

_____

_____

_____

What happened in the story?

_____

_____

_____

_____

_____

_____

Was this book enjoyable?   Yes   No

Would I recommend this book to others?   Yes   No

Other books by this author that I'd like to read:

_____

_____

_____

_____

I read . . .

Title: _____

Author: _____

Sub-genre: _____

Date Published: _____

Date Finished: _____

Rating ○○○○○○○○○○
       1   10

Where I read this book:

_____

_____

_____

How I discovered or received this book:

_____

_____

My favorite spiritual moment in the book:

_____

_____

_____

_____

Delight yourself in the LORD;
And He will give you the desires of your heart.
Psalm 37:4

Who were the characters?

_____

_____

_____

_____

_____

_____

What happened in the story?

_____

_____

_____

_____

_____

_____

Was this book enjoyable?   Yes   No

Would I recommend this book to others?   Yes   No

Other books by this author that I'd like to read:

_____

_____

_____

_____

I read . . .

Title: _____

Author: _____

Sub-genre: _____

Date Published: _____

Date Finished: _____

Rating ○○○○○○○○○○
         1   10

Where I read this book:

_____

_____

_____

How I discovered or received this book:

_____

_____

My favorite spiritual moment in the book:

_____

_____

_____

Rejoice in the Lord always; again I will say, rejoice!
Philippians 4:4

Who were the characters?

_____

_____

_____

_____

_____

_____

What happened in the story?

_____

_____

_____

_____

_____

_____

_____

Was this book enjoyable?   Yes   No

Would I recommend this book to others?   Yes   No

Other books by this author that I'd like to read:

_____

_____

_____

_____

I read . . .

Title: _____

Author: _____

Sub-genre: _____

Date Published: _____

Date Finished: _____

Rating ○○○○○○○○○○
　　　　1　　　　　　　　　　10

Where I read this book:

_____

_____

_____

How I discovered or received this book:

_____

_____

My favorite spiritual moment in the book:

_____

_____

_____

Behold, God is my salvation, I will trust and not be afraid;
For the LORD GOD is my strength and song,
And He has become my salvation."
Isaiah 12:2

Who were the characters?

_____

_____

_____

_____

_____

_____

What happened in the story?

_____

_____

_____

_____

_____

_____

Was this book enjoyable?   Yes   No

Would I recommend this book to others?   Yes   No

Other books by this author that I'd like to read:

_____

_____

_____

_____

I read . . .

Title: _____

Author: _____

Sub-genre: _____

Date Published: _____

Date Finished: _____

Rating ◯◯◯◯◯◯◯◯◯◯
         1   10

Where I read this book:

_____

_____

_____

How I discovered or received this book:

_____

_____

My favorite spiritual moment in the book:

_____

_____

_____

Blessed are the pure in heart, for they shall see God.
Matthew 5:8

Who were the characters?

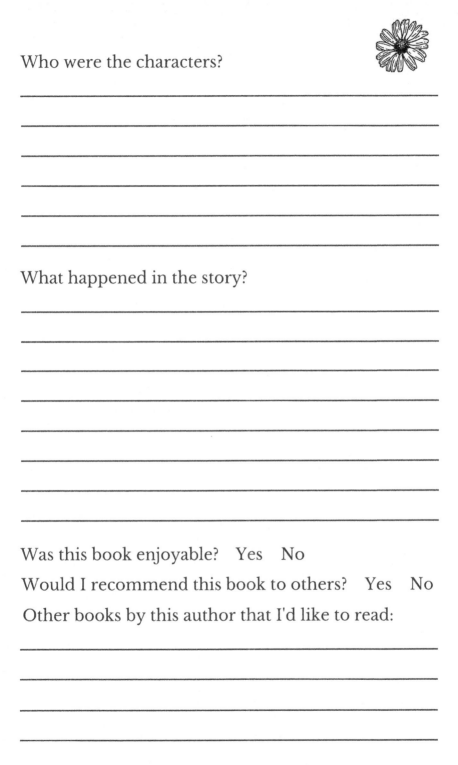

_____

_____

_____

_____

_____

What happened in the story?

_____

_____

_____

_____

_____

_____

Was this book enjoyable?   Yes   No

Would I recommend this book to others?   Yes   No

Other books by this author that I'd like to read:

_____

_____

_____

I read . . .

Title: _____

Author: _____

Sub-genre: _____

Date Published: _____

Date Finished: _____

Rating ○○○○○○○○○○
        1   10

Where I read this book:

_____

_____

_____

How I discovered or received this book:

_____

_____

My favorite spiritual moment in the book:

_____

_____

_____

Blessed are you, Israel!
Who is like you, a people saved by the LORD?
He is your shield and helper and your glorious sword.
Deuteronomy 33:29

Who were the characters?

_____

_____

_____

_____

_____

_____

What happened in the story?

_____

_____

_____

_____

_____

_____

Was this book enjoyable?   Yes   No

Would I recommend this book to others?   Yes   No

Other books by this author that I'd like to read:

_____

_____

_____

_____

I read . . .

Title: _____

Author: _____

Sub-genre: _____

Date Published: _____

Date Finished: _____

Rating ○○○○○○○○○
        1   10

Where I read this book:

_____

_____

_____

How I discovered or received this book:

_____

_____

My favorite spiritual moment in the book:

_____

_____

_____

_____

I delight to do Your will, O my God;
Your Law is within my heart.
Psalm 40:8

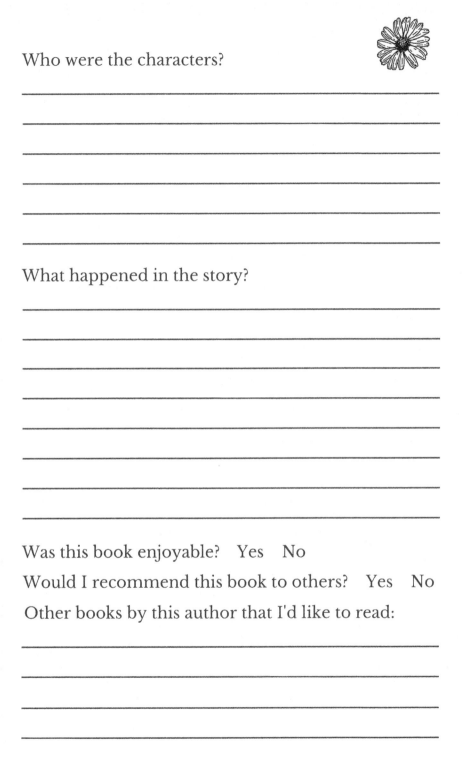

Who were the characters?

_____

_____

_____

_____

_____

What happened in the story?

_____

_____

_____

_____

_____

_____

Was this book enjoyable?   Yes   No

Would I recommend this book to others?   Yes   No

Other books by this author that I'd like to read:

_____

_____

_____

_____

I read . . .

Title: _____

Author: _____

Sub-genre: _____

Date Published: _____

Date Finished: _____

Rating ⭘⭘⭘⭘⭘⭘⭘⭘⭘⭘
        1   10

Where I read this book:

_____

_____

_____

How I discovered or received this book:

_____

_____

My favorite spiritual moment in the book:

_____

_____

_____

_____

Your word is a lamp to my feet And a light to my path.
Psalm 119:105

Who were the characters?

_____

_____

_____

_____

_____

What happened in the story?

_____

_____

_____

_____

_____

_____

Was this book enjoyable?   Yes   No

Would I recommend this book to others?   Yes   No

Other books by this author that I'd like to read:

_____

_____

_____

_____

I read . . .

Title: _____

Author: _____

Sub-genre: _____

Date Published: _____

Date Finished: _____

Rating ○○○○○○○○○○
1   10

Where I read this book:

_____

_____

_____

How I discovered or received this book:

_____

_____

My favorite spiritual moment in the book:

_____

_____

_____

_____

Great are the works of the LORD;
They are studied by all who delight in them.
Psalm 111:2

Who were the characters?

_____

_____

_____

_____

_____

_____

What happened in the story?

_____

_____

_____

_____

_____

_____

_____

Was this book enjoyable?   Yes   No

Would I recommend this book to others?   Yes   No

Other books by this author that I'd like to read:

_____

_____

_____

_____

Favorite Quotes from Books

I read . . .

Title: _____

Author: _____

Sub-genre: _____

Date Published: _____

Date Finished: _____

Rating ◯◯◯◯◯◯◯◯◯◯
         1   10

Where I read this book:

_____

_____

_____

How I discovered or received this book:

_____

_____

My favorite spiritual moment in the book:

_____

_____

_____

Then the LORD your God will prosper you
abundantly in all the work of your hand . . .
Deuteronomy 30:9

Who were the characters?

_____

_____

_____

_____

_____

_____

What happened in the story?

_____

_____

_____

_____

_____

_____

Was this book enjoyable?   Yes   No

Would I recommend this book to others?   Yes   No

Other books by this author that I'd like to read:

_____

_____

_____

_____

I read . . .

Title: _____

Author: _____

Sub-genre: _____

Date Published: _____

Date Finished: _____

Rating ○○○○○○○○○
       1   10

Where I read this book:

_____

_____

_____

How I discovered or received this book:

_____

_____

My favorite spiritual moment in the book:

_____

_____

_____

_____

O taste and see that the LORD is good;
How blessed is the man who takes refuge in Him!
Psalm 34:8

Who were the characters?

_____

_____

_____

_____

_____

_____

What happened in the story?

_____

_____

_____

_____

_____

_____

_____

Was this book enjoyable?   Yes   No

Would I recommend this book to others?   Yes   No

Other books by this author that I'd like to read:

_____

_____

_____

_____

I read . . .

Title: _____

Author: _____

Sub-genre: _____

Date Published: _____

Date Finished: _____

Rating ○○○○○○○○○
1   10

Where I read this book:

_____

_____

_____

How I discovered or received this book:

_____

_____

My favorite spiritual moment in the book:

_____

_____

_____

. . . for the joy of the LORD is your strength.
Nehemiah 8:10

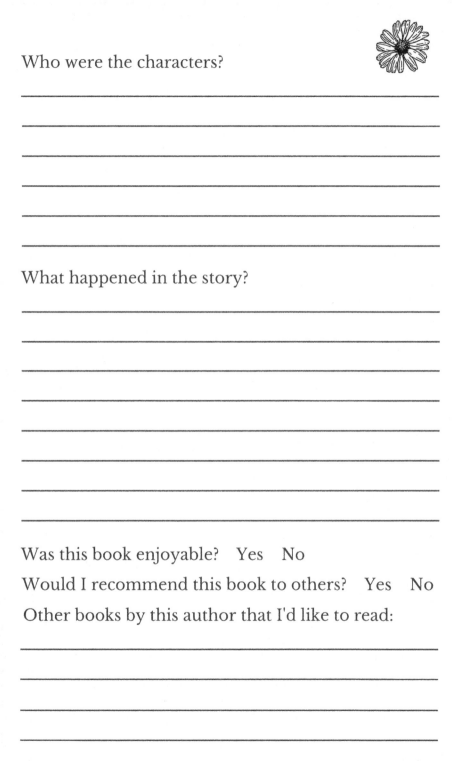

Who were the characters?

_____

_____

_____

_____

_____

_____

What happened in the story?

_____

_____

_____

_____

_____

_____

_____

Was this book enjoyable?   Yes   No

Would I recommend this book to others?   Yes   No

Other books by this author that I'd like to read:

_____

_____

_____

_____

I read . . .

Title: _____

Author: _____

Sub-genre: _____

Date Published: _____

Date Finished: _____

Rating ○○○○○○○○○
        1   10

Where I read this book:

_____

_____

_____

How I discovered or received this book:

_____

_____

My favorite spiritual moment in the book:

_____

_____

_____

_____

I will rejoice greatly in the LORD,
My soul will exult in my God . . .
Isaiah 61:10

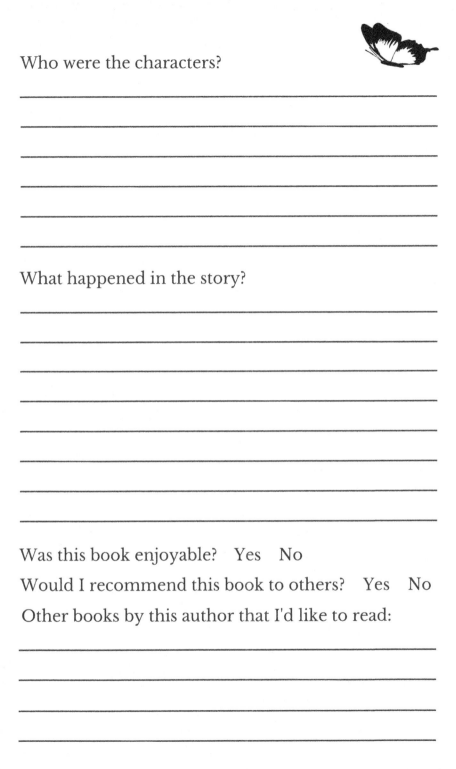

Who were the characters?

_____

_____

_____

_____

_____

_____

What happened in the story?

_____

_____

_____

_____

_____

_____

Was this book enjoyable?   Yes   No

Would I recommend this book to others?   Yes   No

Other books by this author that I'd like to read:

_____

_____

_____

_____

I read . . .

Title: _____

Author: _____

Sub-genre: _____

Date Published: _____

Date Finished: _____

Rating ○○○○○○○○○
       1   10

Where I read this book:

_____

_____

_____

How I discovered or received this book:

_____

_____

My favorite spiritual moment in the book:

_____

_____

_____

_____

A person finds joy in giving an apt reply—
and how good is a timely word! (NIV)
Proverbs 15:23

Who were the characters?

_____

_____

_____

_____

_____

_____

What happened in the story?

_____

_____

_____

_____

_____

_____

_____

Was this book enjoyable?   Yes   No

Would I recommend this book to others?   Yes   No

Other books by this author that I'd like to read:

_____

_____

_____

_____

I read . . .

Title: _____

Author: _____

Sub-genre: _____

Date Published: _____

Date Finished: _____

Rating ◯◯◯◯◯◯◯◯◯◯
       1   10

Where I read this book:

_____

_____

_____

How I discovered or received this book:

_____

_____

My favorite spiritual moment in the book:

_____

_____

_____

. . . I will see you again, and your heart will rejoice,
and no one will take your joy away from you.
John 16:22

Who were the characters?

_____

_____

_____

_____

_____

_____

What happened in the story?

_____

_____

_____

_____

_____

_____

Was this book enjoyable?   Yes   No

Would I recommend this book to others?   Yes   No

Other books by this author that I'd like to read:

_____

_____

_____

_____

I read . . .

Title: _____

Author: _____

Sub-genre: _____

Date Published: _____

Date Finished: _____

Rating ◯◯◯◯◯◯◯◯◯◯
　　　　1　　　　　　　　　　10

Where I read this book:

_____

_____

_____

How I discovered or received this book:

_____

_____

My favorite spiritual moment in the book:

_____

_____

_____

He who dwells in the shelter of the Most High Will
abide in the shadow of the Almighty.
Psalm 91:1

Who were the characters?

_____

_____

_____

_____

_____

_____

What happened in the story?

_____

_____

_____

_____

_____

_____

_____

Was this book enjoyable?   Yes   No

Would I recommend this book to others?   Yes   No

Other books by this author that I'd like to read:

_____

_____

_____

_____

I read . . .

Title: _____

Author: _____

Sub-genre: _____

Date Published: _____

Date Finished: _____

Rating ○○○○○○○○○○
1   10

Where I read this book:

_____

_____

_____

How I discovered or received this book:

_____

_____

My favorite spiritual moment in the book:

_____

_____

_____

*Now to Him who is able to do far more abundantly
beyond all that we ask or think,
according to the power that works within us . . .*
Ephesians 3:20

Who were the characters?

_____

_____

_____

_____

_____

_____

What happened in the story?

_____

_____

_____

_____

_____

_____

_____

Was this book enjoyable?   Yes   No

Would I recommend this book to others?   Yes   No

Other books by this author that I'd like to read:

_____

_____

_____

_____

I read . . .

Title: _____

Author: _____

Sub-genre: _____

Date Published: _____

Date Finished: _____

Rating ○○○○○○○○○
      1   10

Where I read this book:

_____

_____

_____

How I discovered or received this book:

_____

_____

My favorite spiritual moment in the book:

_____

_____

_____

O clap your hands, all peoples;
Shout to God with the voice of joy.
Psalm 47:1

Who were the characters?

_____

_____

_____

_____

_____

What happened in the story?

_____

_____

_____

_____

_____

Was this book enjoyable?   Yes   No

Would I recommend this book to others?   Yes   No

Other books by this author that I'd like to read:

_____

_____

_____

I read . . .

Title:_____

Author: _____

Sub-genre:_____

Date Published:_____

Date Finished:_____

Rating ○○○○○○○○○○
      1   10

Where I read this book:

_____

_____

_____

How I discovered or received this book:

_____

_____

My favorite spiritual moment in the book:

_____

_____

_____

. . . and the people were playing on flutes and rejoicing with great joy, so that the earth shook at their noise.
1 Kings 1:40

Who were the characters?

_____

_____

_____

_____

_____

_____

What happened in the story?

_____

_____

_____

_____

_____

_____

_____

Was this book enjoyable?   Yes   No

Would I recommend this book to others?   Yes   No

Other books by this author that I'd like to read:

_____

_____

_____

_____

I read . . .

Title: _____

Author: _____

Sub-genre: _____

Date Published: _____

Date Finished: _____

Rating ○○○○○○○○○
       1   10

Where I read this book:

_____

_____

_____

How I discovered or received this book:

_____

_____

My favorite spiritual moment in the book:

_____

_____

_____

We will sing for joy over your victory,
And in the name of our God we will set up our banners.
May the LORD fulfill all your petitions.
Psalm 20:5

Who were the characters?

_____

_____

_____

_____

_____

_____

What happened in the story?

_____

_____

_____

_____

_____

_____

Was this book enjoyable?   Yes   No

Would I recommend this book to others?   Yes   No

Other books by this author that I'd like to read:

_____

_____

_____

_____

I read . . .

Title:_____

Author: _____

Sub-genre:_____

Date Published: _____

Date Finished:_____

Rating ◯◯◯◯◯◯◯◯◯◯
       1   10

Where I read this book:

_____

_____

_____

How I discovered or received this book:

_____

_____

My favorite spiritual moment in the book:

_____

_____

_____

_____

They raise their voices, they shout for joy; They cry out from the west concerning the majesty of the LORD .

Psalm 147:1

Who were the characters?

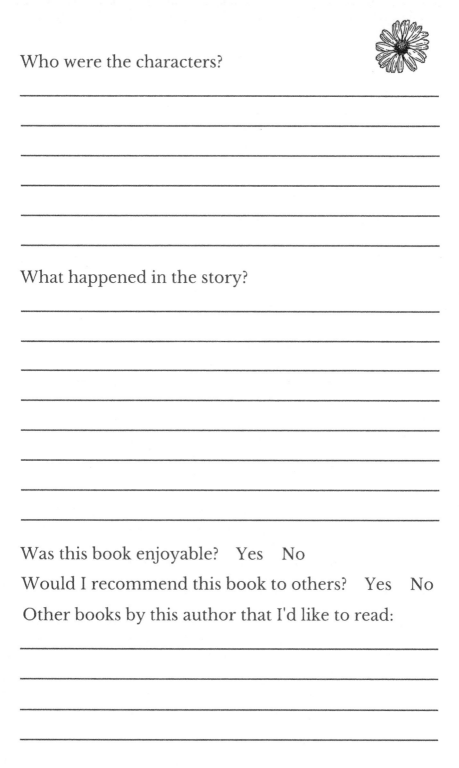

_____

_____

_____

_____

_____

_____

What happened in the story?

_____

_____

_____

_____

_____

_____

_____

Was this book enjoyable?   Yes   No

Would I recommend this book to others?   Yes   No

Other books by this author that I'd like to read:

_____

_____

_____

_____

I read . . .

Title:_____

Author: _____

Sub-genre:_____

Date Published:_____

Date Finished:_____

Rating ◯◯◯◯◯◯◯◯◯◯
　　　　1　　　　　　　　　　10

Where I read this book:

_____

_____

_____

How I discovered or received this book:

_____

_____

My favorite spiritual moment in the book:

_____

_____

_____

_____

It will blossom profusely
And rejoice with rejoicing and shout of joy.
Isaiah 35:2

Who were the characters?

_____

_____

_____

_____

_____

_____

What happened in the story?

_____

_____

_____

_____

_____

_____

_____

Was this book enjoyable?   Yes   No

Would I recommend this book to others?   Yes   No

Other books by this author that I'd like to read:

_____

_____

_____

_____

I read . . .

Title:_____

Author: _____

Sub-genre:_____

Date Published: _____

Date Finished:_____

Rating ◯◯◯◯◯◯◯◯◯◯
      1   10

Where I read this book:

_____

_____

_____

How I discovered or received this book:

_____

_____

My favorite spiritual moment in the book:

_____

_____

_____

_____

I have no greater joy than this,
to hear of my children walking in the truth.
3 John 1:4

Who were the characters?

_____

_____

_____

_____

_____

What happened in the story?

_____

_____

_____

_____

_____

_____

Was this book enjoyable?   Yes   No

Would I recommend this book to others?   Yes   No

Other books by this author that I'd like to read:

_____

_____

_____

_____

I read . . .

Title: _____

Author: _____

Sub-genre: _____

Date Published: _____

Date Finished: _____

Rating ○○○○○○○○○○
        1   10

Where I read this book:

_____

_____

_____

How I discovered or received this book:

_____

_____

My favorite spiritual moment in the book:

_____

_____

_____

But the fruit of the Spirit is love, joy, peace, patience,
kindness, goodness, faithfulness, gentleness, self-control;
against such things there is no law.
Galatians 5:22-23

Who were the characters?

_____

_____

_____

_____

_____

_____

What happened in the story?

_____

_____

_____

_____

_____

_____

Was this book enjoyable?   Yes   No

Would I recommend this book to others?   Yes   No

Other books by this author that I'd like to read:

_____

_____

_____

_____

I read . . .

Title: _____

Author: _____

Sub-genre: _____

Date Published: _____

Date Finished: _____

Rating ○○○○○○○○○
1   10

Where I read this book:

_____

_____

_____

How I discovered or received this book:

_____

_____

My favorite spiritual moment in the book:

_____

_____

_____

_____

*And suddenly there appeared with the angel a multitude of the
heavenly host praising God and saying, "Glory to God in the
highest, And on earth peace among men with whom He is pleased."*
Luke 2:13-14

Who were the characters?

_____

_____

_____

_____

_____

_____

What happened in the story?

_____

_____

_____

_____

_____

_____

_____

Was this book enjoyable?   Yes   No

Would I recommend this book to others?   Yes   No

Other books by this author that I'd like to read:

_____

_____

_____

_____

I read . . .

Title: _____

Author: _____

Sub-genre: _____

Date Published: _____

Date Finished: _____

Rating ◯◯◯◯◯◯◯◯◯◯
        1   10

Where I read this book:

_____

_____

_____

How I discovered or received this book:

_____

_____

My favorite spiritual moment in the book:

_____

_____

_____

_____

For His anger is but for a moment, His favor is for a
lifetime; Weeping may last for the night, But a shout of joy
comes in the morning.
Psalm 30:5

Who were the characters?

_____

_____

_____

_____

_____

_____

What happened in the story?

_____

_____

_____

_____

_____

_____

_____

Was this book enjoyable?   Yes   No

Would I recommend this book to others?   Yes   No

Other books by this author that I'd like to read:

_____

_____

_____

_____

I read . . .

Title: _____

Author: _____

Sub-genre: _____

Date Published: _____

Date Finished: _____

Rating ◯◯◯◯◯◯◯◯◯◯
1   10

Where I read this book:

_____

_____

_____

How I discovered or received this book:

_____

_____

My favorite spiritual moment in the book:

_____

_____

_____

*Praise the LORD! How blessed is the man who fears the
LORD, Who greatly delights in His commandments.*
Psalm 112:1

Who were the characters?

_____

_____

_____

_____

_____

_____

What happened in the story?

_____

_____

_____

_____

_____

_____

_____

Was this book enjoyable?   Yes   No

Would I recommend this book to others?   Yes   No

Other books by this author that I'd like to read:

_____

_____

_____

_____

I read . . .

Title: _____

Author: _____

Sub-genre: _____

Date Published: _____

Date Finished: _____

Rating ○○○○○○○○○○
       1   10

Where I read this book:

_____

_____

_____

How I discovered or received this book:

_____

_____

My favorite spiritual moment in the book:

_____

_____

_____

These things I have spoken to you so
that My joy may be in you, and that
your joy may be made full.
John 15:11

Who were the characters?

_____

_____

_____

_____

_____

_____

What happened in the story?

_____

_____

_____

_____

_____

_____

Was this book enjoyable?   Yes   No

Would I recommend this book to others?   Yes   No

Other books by this author that I'd like to read:

_____

_____

_____

_____

I read . . .

Title: _____

Author: _____

Sub-genre: _____

Date Published: _____

Date Finished: _____

Rating ○○○○○○○○○
         1   10

Where I read this book:

_____

_____

_____

How I discovered or received this book:

_____

_____

My favorite spiritual moment in the book:

_____

_____

_____

_____

For you will go out with joy And be led forth with peace;
The mountains and the hills will break forth into shouts of joy
before you, And all the trees of the field will clap their hands.
Isaiah 55:12

Who were the characters?

_____

_____

_____

_____

_____

_____

What happened in the story?

_____

_____

_____

_____

_____

_____

_____

Was this book enjoyable?   Yes   No

Would I recommend this book to others?   Yes   No

Other books by this author that I'd like to read:

_____

_____

_____

_____

A Time or Place From a Book That I'd Like to Visit

What book inspired you?

When or where would you like to visit?

Why?

What book inspired you?

When or where would you like to visit?

Why?

What book inspired you?

_____

When or where would you like to visit?

_____

_____

_____

Why?

_____

_____

_____

What book inspired you?

_____

When or where would you like to visit?

_____

_____

_____

Why?

_____

_____

_____

I read . . .

Title: _____

Author: _____

Sub-genre: _____

Date Published: _____

Date Finished: _____

Rating ○○○○○○○○○
         1   10

Where I read this book:

_____

_____

_____

How I discovered or received this book:

_____

_____

My favorite spiritual moment in the book:

_____

_____

_____

_____

The LORD your God is in your midst, A victorious warrior. He will exult over you with joy, He will be quiet in His love, He will rejoice over you with shouts of joy.
Zephaniah 3:17

Who were the characters?

_____

_____

_____

_____

_____

_____

What happened in the story?

_____

_____

_____

_____

_____

_____

Was this book enjoyable?   Yes   No

Would I recommend this book to others?   Yes   No

Other books by this author that I'd like to read:

_____

_____

_____

_____

I read . . .

Title: _____

Author: _____

Sub-genre: _____

Date Published: _____

Date Finished: _____

Rating ○○○○○○○○○
      1   10

Where I read this book:

_____

_____

_____

How I discovered or received this book:

_____

_____

My favorite spiritual moment in the book:

_____

_____

_____

_____

Yet I will exult in the LORD,
I will rejoice in the God of my salvation.
Habakkuk 3:18

Who were the characters?

_____

_____

_____

_____

_____

What happened in the story?

_____

_____

_____

_____

_____

_____

Was this book enjoyable?   Yes   No

Would I recommend this book to others?   Yes   No

Other books by this author that I'd like to read:

_____

_____

_____

_____

I read . . .

Title: _____

Author: _____

Sub-genre: _____

Date Published: _____

Date Finished: _____

Rating ○○○○○○○○○
       1   10

Where I read this book:

_____

_____

_____

How I discovered or received this book:

_____

_____

My favorite spiritual moment in the book:

_____

_____

_____

_____

Delight yourself in the LORD;
And He will give you the desires of your heart.
Psalm 37:4

Who were the characters?

_____

_____

_____

_____

_____

What happened in the story?

_____

_____

_____

_____

_____

_____

Was this book enjoyable?   Yes   No

Would I recommend this book to others?   Yes   No

Other books by this author that I'd like to read:

_____

_____

_____

_____

I read . . .

Title:_____

Author: _____

Sub-genre:_____

Date Published:_____

Date Finished:_____

Rating ◯◯◯◯◯◯◯◯◯◯
        1   10

Where I read this book:

_____

_____

_____

How I discovered or received this book:

_____

_____

My favorite spiritual moment in the book:

_____

_____

_____

_____

And now my head will be lifted up above my enemies around me, And I will offer in His tent sacrifices with shouts of joy; I will sing, yes, I will sing praises to the LORD.
Psalm 27:6

Who were the characters?

_____

_____

_____

_____

_____

_____

What happened in the story?

_____

_____

_____

_____

_____

_____

Was this book enjoyable?   Yes   No

Would I recommend this book to others?   Yes   No

Other books by this author that I'd like to read:

_____

_____

_____

_____

I read . . .

Title: _____

Author: _____

Sub-genre: _____

Date Published: _____

Date Finished: _____

Rating ○○○○○○○○○○
       1   10

Where I read this book:

_____

_____

_____

How I discovered or received this book:

_____

_____

My favorite spiritual moment in the book:

_____

_____

_____

Shout joyfully to the LORD, all the earth;
Break forth and sing for joy and sing praises.
Psalm 98:4

Who were the characters?

_____

_____

_____

_____

_____

_____

What happened in the story?

_____

_____

_____

_____

_____

_____

Was this book enjoyable?   Yes   No

Would I recommend this book to others?   Yes   No

Other books by this author that I'd like to read:

_____

_____

_____

_____

I read . . .

Title: _____

Author: _____

Sub-genre: _____

Date Published: _____

Date Finished: _____

Rating ○○○○○○○○○○
1   10

Where I read this book:

_____

_____

_____

How I discovered or received this book:

_____

_____

My favorite spiritual moment in the book:

_____

_____

_____

*The thief comes only to steal and kill and destroy; I have
come that they may have life, and have it to the full.* (NIV)
John 10:10

Who were the characters?

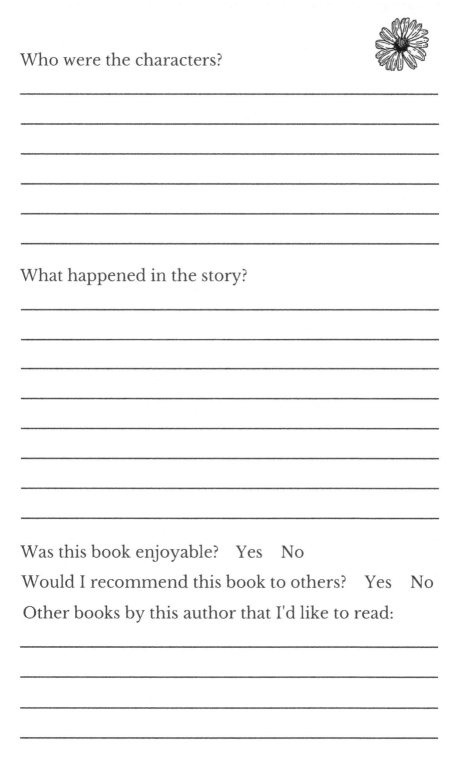

_____

_____

_____

_____

_____

_____

What happened in the story?

_____

_____

_____

_____

_____

_____

_____

Was this book enjoyable?   Yes   No

Would I recommend this book to others?   Yes   No

Other books by this author that I'd like to read:

_____

_____

_____

_____

I read . . .

Title: _____

Author: _____

Sub-genre: _____

Date Published: _____

Date Finished: _____

Rating ◯◯◯◯◯◯◯◯◯◯
        1   10

Where I read this book:

_____

_____

_____

How I discovered or received this book:

_____

_____

My favorite spiritual moment in the book:

_____

_____

_____

_____

*I know that there is nothing better for people than to be happy
and to do good while they live.* (NIV)
Ecclesiastes 3:12

Who were the characters?

_____

_____

_____

_____

_____

_____

What happened in the story?

_____

_____

_____

_____

_____

_____

_____

Was this book enjoyable?   Yes   No

Would I recommend this book to others?   Yes   No

Other books by this author that I'd like to read:

_____

_____

_____

_____

I read . . .

Title: _____

Author: _____

Sub-genre: _____

Date Published: _____

Date Finished: _____

Rating ○○○○○○○○○○
      1   10

Where I read this book:

_____

_____

_____

How I discovered or received this book:

_____

_____

My favorite spiritual moment in the book:

_____

_____

_____

_____

Sing to Him a new song; Play skillfully with a shout of joy.
Psalm 33:3

Who were the characters?

_____

_____

_____

_____

_____

_____

What happened in the story?

_____

_____

_____

_____

_____

_____

Was this book enjoyable?   Yes   No

Would I recommend this book to others?   Yes   No

Other books by this author that I'd like to read:

_____

_____

_____

_____

I read . . .

Title: _____

Author: _____

Sub-genre: _____

Date Published: _____

Date Finished: _____

Rating ◯◯◯◯◯◯◯◯◯
      1   10

Where I read this book:

_____

_____

_____

How I discovered or received this book:

_____

_____

My favorite spiritual moment in the book:

_____

_____

_____

Be glad in the LORD and rejoice, you righteous ones; And
shout for joy, all you who are upright in heart.
Psalm 32:11

Who were the characters?

_____

_____

_____

_____

_____

_____

What happened in the story?

_____

_____

_____

_____

_____

_____

Was this book enjoyable?   Yes   No

Would I recommend this book to others?   Yes   No

Other books by this author that I'd like to read:

_____

_____

_____

_____

I read . . .

Title: _____

Author: _____

Sub-genre: _____

Date Published: _____

Date Finished: _____

Rating ○○○○○○○○○○
1   10

Where I read this book:

_____

_____

_____

How I discovered or received this book:

_____

_____

My favorite spiritual moment in the book:

_____

_____

_____

*Rejoice always; pray without ceasing; in everything give
thanks; for this is God's will for you in Christ Jesus.*
1 Thessalonians 5:16-18

Who were the characters?

_____

_____

_____

_____

_____

_____

What happened in the story?

_____

_____

_____

_____

_____

_____

Was this book enjoyable?   Yes   No

Would I recommend this book to others?   Yes   No

Other books by this author that I'd like to read:

_____

_____

_____

_____

I read . . .

Title: _____

Author: _____

Sub-genre: _____

Date Published: _____

Date Finished:_____

Rating ○○○○○○○○○○
　　　　1　　　　　　　　　　10

Where I read this book:

_____

_____

_____

How I discovered or received this book:

_____

_____

My favorite spiritual moment in the book:

_____

_____

_____

Until now you have asked for nothing in My name; ask and
you will receive, so that your joy may be made full.
John 16:24

Who were the characters?

_____

_____

_____

_____

_____

_____

What happened in the story?

_____

_____

_____

_____

_____

_____

Was this book enjoyable?   Yes   No

Would I recommend this book to others?   Yes   No

Other books by this author that I'd like to read:

_____

_____

_____

_____

I read . . .

Title: _____

Author: _____

Sub-genre: _____

Date Published: _____

Date Finished: _____

Rating ◯◯◯◯◯◯◯◯◯◯
1   10

Where I read this book:

_____

_____

_____

How I discovered or received this book:

_____

_____

My favorite spiritual moment in the book:

_____

_____

_____

The righteous man will be glad in the LORD
and will take refuge in Him;
And all the upright in heart will glory.
Psalm 64:10

Who were the characters?

_____

_____

_____

_____

_____

_____

What happened in the story?

_____

_____

_____

_____

_____

_____

_____

Was this book enjoyable?   Yes   No

Would I recommend this book to others?   Yes   No

Other books by this author that I'd like to read:

_____

_____

_____

_____

I read . . .

Title: _____

Author: _____

Sub-genre: _____

Date Published: _____

Date Finished: _____

Rating ○○○○○○○○○
         1   10

Where I read this book:

_____

_____

_____

How I discovered or received this book:

_____

_____

My favorite spiritual moment in the book:

_____

_____

_____

_____

Light is sown like seed for the righteous
And gladness for the upright in heart.
Psalm 97:11

Who were the characters?

_____

_____

_____

_____

_____

What happened in the story?

_____

_____

_____

_____

_____

_____

Was this book enjoyable?   Yes   No

Would I recommend this book to others?   Yes   No

Other books by this author that I'd like to read:

_____

_____

_____

I read . . .

Title: _____

Author: _____

Sub-genre: _____

Date Published: _____

Date Finished: _____

Rating ◯◯◯◯◯◯◯◯◯◯
　　　　1　　　　　　　　　　　10

Where I read this book:

_____

_____

_____

How I discovered or received this book:

_____

_____

My favorite spiritual moment in the book:

_____

_____

_____

And the peace of God, which surpasses all comprehension,
will guard your hearts and your minds in Christ Jesus.
Philippians 4:7

Who were the characters?

_____

_____

_____

_____

_____

_____

What happened in the story?

_____

_____

_____

_____

_____

_____

Was this book enjoyable?   Yes   No

Would I recommend this book to others?   Yes   No

Other books by this author that I'd like to read:

_____

_____

_____

_____

I read . . .

Title: _____

Author: _____

Sub-genre: _____

Date Published: _____

Date Finished: _____

Rating ◯◯◯◯◯◯◯◯◯◯
      1   10

Where I read this book:

_____

_____

_____

How I discovered or received this book:

_____

_____

My favorite spiritual moment in the book:

_____

_____

_____

_____

Now may the God of hope fill you with all joy and peace in believing, so that you will abound in hope by the power of the Holy Spirit.
Romans 15:13

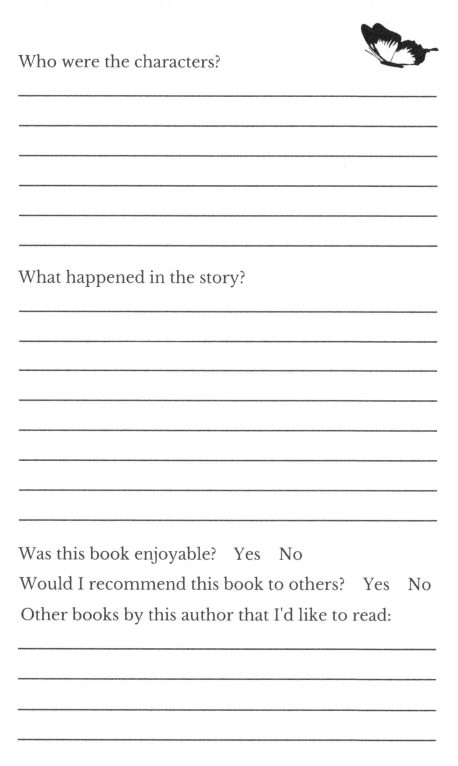

Who were the characters?

_____

_____

_____

_____

_____

_____

What happened in the story?

_____

_____

_____

_____

_____

_____

Was this book enjoyable?   Yes   No

Would I recommend this book to others?   Yes   No

Other books by this author that I'd like to read:

_____

_____

_____

_____

I read . . .

Title: _____

Author: _____

Sub-genre: _____

Date Published: _____

Date Finished: _____

Rating ◯◯◯◯◯◯◯◯◯◯
        1   10

Where I read this book:

_____

_____

_____

How I discovered or received this book:

_____

_____

My favorite spiritual moment in the book:

_____

_____

_____

Let the heavens be glad, and let the earth rejoice; And let them say among the nations, "The LORD reigns."
1 Chronicles 16:31

Who were the characters?

_____

_____

_____

_____

_____

_____

What happened in the story?

_____

_____

_____

_____

_____

_____

_____

Was this book enjoyable?   Yes   No

Would I recommend this book to others?   Yes   No

Other books by this author that I'd like to read:

_____

_____

_____

_____

I read . . .

Title: _____

Author: _____

Sub-genre: _____

Date Published: _____

Date Finished: _____

Rating ◯◯◯◯◯◯◯◯◯◯
        1   10

Where I read this book:

_____

_____

_____

How I discovered or received this book:

_____

_____

My favorite spiritual moment in the book:

_____

_____

_____

_____

Shout joyfully to God, all the earth;
Sing the glory of His name; Make His praise glorious.
Psalm 66:1-2

Who were the characters?

_____

_____

_____

_____

_____

_____

What happened in the story?

_____

_____

_____

_____

_____

_____

Was this book enjoyable?　Yes　No

Would I recommend this book to others?　Yes　No

Other books by this author that I'd like to read:

_____

_____

_____

_____

I read . . .

Title: _____

Author: _____

Sub-genre: _____

Date Published: _____

Date Finished: _____

Rating ○○○○○○○○○○
1   10

Where I read this book:

_____

_____

_____

How I discovered or received this book:

_____

_____

My favorite spiritual moment in the book:

_____

_____

_____

O satisfy us in the morning with Your lovingkindness,
That we may sing for joy and be glad all our days.
Psalm 90:14

Who were the characters?

_____

_____

_____

_____

_____

_____

What happened in the story?

_____

_____

_____

_____

_____

_____

Was this book enjoyable?   Yes   No

Would I recommend this book to others?   Yes   No

Other books by this author that I'd like to read:

_____

_____

_____

_____

I read . . .

Title: _____

Author: _____

Sub-genre: _____

Date Published: _____

Date Finished: _____

Rating ⃝⃝⃝⃝⃝⃝⃝⃝⃝⃝
      1   10

Where I read this book:

_____

_____

_____

How I discovered or received this book:

_____

_____

My favorite spiritual moment in the book:

_____

_____

_____

But let all who take refuge in You be glad,
Let them ever sing for joy; And may You shelter them,
That those who love Your name may exult in You.
Psalm 5:11

Who were the characters?

_____

_____

_____

_____

_____

_____

What happened in the story?

_____

_____

_____

_____

_____

_____

Was this book enjoyable?   Yes   No

Would I recommend this book to others?   Yes   No

Other books by this author that I'd like to read:

_____

_____

_____

_____

I read . . .

Title: _____

Author: _____

Sub-genre: _____

Date Published: _____

Date Finished: _____

Rating ○○○○○○○○○
       1   10

Where I read this book:

_____

_____

_____

How I discovered or received this book:

_____

_____

My favorite spiritual moment in the book:

_____

_____

_____

*Let all who seek You rejoice and be glad in You; Let those
who love Your salvation say continually,
"The LORD be magnified!"*
Psalm 40:16

Who were the characters?

_____

_____

_____

_____

_____

_____

What happened in the story?

_____

_____

_____

_____

_____

_____

Was this book enjoyable?   Yes   No

Would I recommend this book to others?   Yes   No

Other books by this author that I'd like to read:

_____

_____

_____

_____

Books I would share with a friend who . . .

. . .wants to deepen their faith

_____

_____

_____

_____

_____

_____

_____

_____

_____

_____

_____

_____

_____

_____

_____

_____

_____

_____

_____

You are my hiding place;
You preserve me from trouble;
You surround me with songs of deliverance.
Psalms 32:7

... needs a smile

_____

_____

_____

_____

_____

_____

_____

_____

_____

_____

_____

_____

_____

_____

_____

_____

_____

_____

_____

A joyful heart is good medicine . . .
Proverbs 17:22

. . .wants an adventure

_____

_____

_____

_____

_____

_____

_____

_____

_____

_____

_____

_____

_____

_____

_____

_____

_____

_____

Until now you have asked for nothing in My name;
ask and you will receive,
so that your joy may be made full.
John 16:24

... wants to visit another time

_____

_____

_____

_____

_____

_____

_____

_____

_____

_____

_____

_____

_____

_____

_____

_____

_____

_____

_____

_____

_____

_____

Therefore my heart is glad and my glory rejoices . .
Psalm 16:9

Books I Want to Read

How you learned about a book is part of the fun.
Write the title and that person or place below.

Title: _____

How: _____

Title: _____

How: _____

Title: _____

How: _____

Title: _____

How: _____

Title: _____

How: _____

Title: _____

How: _____

Title: _____

How: _____

Title: _____

How: _____

Title: _____

How: _____

Title: _____
How: _____
Title: _____
How: _____
Title: _____
How: _____
Title: _____
How: _____
Title: _____
How: _____
Title: _____
How: _____
Title: _____
How: _____
Title: _____
How: _____
Title: _____
How: _____
Title: _____
How: _____
Title: _____
How: _____
Title: _____
How: _____

Books I Want to Read

How you learned about a book is part of the fun.
Write the title and that person or place below.

Title: _____

How: _____

Title: _____

How: _____

Title: _____

How: _____

Title: _____

How: _____

Title: _____

How: _____

Title: _____

How: _____

Title: _____

How: _____

Title: _____

How: _____

Title: _____

How: _____

Title: _____

How: _____

Title:

How:

Title:

How:

Title:

How:

Title:

How:

Title:

How:

Title:

How:

Title:

How:

Title:

How:

Title:

How:

Title:

How:

Title:

How:

Title:

How:

Books Loaned

Title	Person	Date

Books Loaned

Title	Person	Date

Books Borrowed

Title	Person	Date

Books Borrowed

Title	Person	Date

Notes

Other Books by Cathryn Brown

Clean and wholesome books with
Christian main characters

Alaska Dream Romance Series

Falling for Alaska
Loving Alaska
Merrying in Alaska
Crazy About Alaska

By Shannon L. Brown

Crime-Solving Cousins Mysteries

The Feather Chase
The Treasure Key
The Chocolate Spy

To learn more about me or my books,
please visit www.cathrynbrown.com.

Notes